CLUB 7
Sunshine

Wise Publications
London / New York / Paris / Sydney / Copenhagen / Berlin / Madrid / Tokyo

Don't Stop Movin'

Words & Music by Simon Ellis, Sheppard Solomon & S Club 7

Verse 3:
You can touch the moment almost feel it in the air
Don't know where we're goin' baby we don't even care
Ain't no mystery, just use your imagination
Let it take you there
And just go with the magic baby
I can see it there in your eyes
Let it flow, stop the waiting, right here on the dance floor
Is where you gotta let it go.

Don't stop movin' can you feel the music *etc.*

Show Me Your Colours

Words & Music by David Eriksen & Aleena

You cast a spell ov-er me, don't know where to turn_ to a-ny-more. I see your face_

show me your col - ours, show me, don't break this spell I'm in, please don't break my heart.__ Show

me,__ show me your col - ours ba - by, tell me who you real - ly are.__

I know you want what I want, far a - way, but

still with - in our reach. Do you dare,__ are you brave e - nough to show me what your

You

Words & Music by Eliot Kennedy, Tim Lever, Mike Percy & Tim Woodcock

You are all I need to get me through. (To get me through. now ba- by.) Like a fall- ing star I fell for you. (I fell for you.) 1. Sweet an- ti- ci- pa- tion is

(Verse 2 see block lyric)

Verse 2:
I thought I knew what love was
It always ended up in tears
It's just the way my world was
Until you walked into my life
It's something that I just can't hide.

Bridge 2 & 3:
Real love has come my way
And I know that it's here to stay
And it feels like never before
'Cause loving you's so beautiful baby,

'Cause you *etc.*

Good Times

Words & Music by Jonathan Shorten, Eddie Chacon & John Themis

Verse 2:
The pressure's on
Boss is breathing down your neck.
But the only thing you'll see's
That vacation pamphlet on your desk.
You fantasise
The day you'll leave it all behind
To spend the best days of your life
Just lying in the sun.

We all got to change once in a while
The time to make a change is right now.

Boy Like You

Words & Music by Cathy Dennis & Lauren Christie

Hey boy! what you need is a girl who can give you what you need a cra-zy girl,_ some-one like me

1. Oh boy, you're sin-gle and free, you like to play hard, live dan-ger-ous-ly

(Verse 2 see block lyric)

boy like you needs a cra - zy girl____ like me. That a

boy like you needs a cra - zy girl____ like me.

Verse 2:
It's no joke, it's funny to be
Staring at you but all I'm seeing is me.
Like you, I like to live loud,
If you're looking for a good time, look what you've found.
It's fun spending hard cash
But it's over in a flash.
What you need is someone like me
Who's gonna blow your pretty world for free.

Have You Ever

Words & Music by Cathy Dennis, Andrew Frampton & Christopher Braide

1. Some-times it's wrong to walk a-way,_ though you think it's ov-er,
(Verse 2 see block lyric)

know-ing there's so much more to say_ sud-den-ly the mo-ment's_ gone_ and all your

dreams are up-side down,_ and you just wan-na change_ the way_ the world_ goes round._ Tell me

have you ev-er loved and lost some-bo-dy, wished there was a chance to say I'm sor-ry,

can't you_ see_____ that's the way I feel_ a-bout you and me, ba-by

have you ev-er felt your heart was break-ing, look-ing down the road you should be tak-ing,

holding on some-how, wishing I could change the way the world goes round.

Tell me have you ev-er loved and lost some-bo-dy

wished there was a chance to say I'm sor-ry, can't you see that's the

way I feel a-bout you and me ba-by have you ev-er felt your heart was break-ing,

Verse 2:
Can't help but think that this is wrong
We should be together
Back in your arms where I belong.
Now I've finally realised
It was forever that I've found
I'd give it all to change the way the world goes round.

Sunshine

Words & Music by Cathy Dennis, Yak Bondy & S Club 7

-mor - row___ would bring._____ _____ 1. Then you came___

(Verse 2 see block lyric)

___ a - long,___ changed my world___ a - round._____

Gave me some - thing to be - lieve in when I'm up - side down.___

And let___ me say___ I owe___

Verse 2:
If you should find
You need someone too
Just turn, head in my direction
And I'l do the same for you.

And let me say
From the bottom of my heart
I wanna thank you
For making the sun come shining through.

Dance Dance Dance

Words & Music by Cathy Dennis, Jewels & Stone

woo_____ woo_____ woo_____ woo_____

woo_____ woo._____

1. I know a place where the
(Verse 2 see block lyric)

mood is just right, they got the vibe and they're pump - ing it all night.

Where the heat is high and the lights are low, and when you want it, it's the

Verse 2:
It's everywhere, it's in everything
We're getting down and the whole place is moving.
Feel the music pump, hear the vinyl scream
Run to your mama if I scare you with my funky thing.

It's Alright

Words & Music by Eliot Kennedy, Tim Lever, Mike Percy & Tim Woodcock

1. So tell me how you
(Verse 2 see block lyric)

won't you tell me it'll be al - right,_____ don't you know it's gon - na be al - right,_____

please tell me it'll be al - right._____

When you're feel - ing_____ low_____ and you're

on your_____ own,_____ got no - where to_____ go,_____

now's the time to get your-self___ to-ge-ther._____ It's___ al-right,___ a-ny-thing you wan-na. It's___ al-right,___ leav-ing all your trou--bles far___ be-hind,___ don't let a-ny-bo-dy tell___ you how to live___ your life.___ 'Cause it's al-right,___ no mat-ter what your feel - ing. It's___ al-right,___

Repeat to fade

Verse 2:
You gotta understand now
Tomorrow is a brighter day
The memories'll fade away
And the sun will shine on you.

So many friends you've yet to make
So many hearts you've yet to break
So much love you've got to give
Your whole life's still left to live.

Spread your wings and fly
Kiss the pain goodbye
Let the tears run dry
You gotta get yourself together.

Stronger

Words & Music by Simon Ellis, Ryan Molloy & S Club 7

now that I got_ you ba - by. I'm feel - ing strong - er, I'm feel - ing strong - er.____

All stand up, stand up, stand up now. All stand up, let the

mu - sic take you._ 2. Ex - pec - All stand up, stand up, stand up.

All stand up, stand up stand up now. All stand up, stand

Verse 2:
Expectation, no relation
Superstition, no addictions.
You're outrageous but contagious
I'm the fever that won't leave ya.

Right Guy

Words & Music by Cathy Dennis & Bradley McIntosh

La la la la la la la la la la la la la la la la la la.

70

Verse 2:
Girl, you know I got my eyes on you
That's right, I'm talking to you, it's a fantasy what you do to me.
And girl, you know I've got to be with you
Send shivers running down my spine when I think of how you could be mine.

I Will Find You

Words & Music by Yak Bondy & Bradley McIntosh

tell me who. tell me where? 'Cause wher-ev-er I am wher-ev-er you are, I will find you girl, near or far.

1. I fell in love___ with this girl I___ saw,___ and I'm pret - ty sure that me and her have
(Verse 2 see block lyric)

met be - fore.___ So why did I act so shy and did-n't say a thing, 'Cause

now I'm___ won - der - ing_____ oh._____

I've been

Verse 2:
I saw this boy and he looked at me
I noticed him but he didn't notice me.
Why did I act so shy and didn't say a thing?
'Cause now I'm wondering.

Summertime Feeling

Words & Music by Mark Hadfield, Adam Ryan-Carter, S Club 7 & Christine McVie

Got me dream - ing, S - Club feel - ing.

Ah. _____

Got that sum - mer - time _ feel - ing.

1. Slow down 'cause you move too fast, close your eyes and let the day go past.
(Verse 2 see block lyric)

L.H. tacet 1°

Feel - ing the sun and the breeze in your hair, let the waves take a - way your cares.

I'm feel - ing good to - day,_ I just wan - na lis - ten what the flow - ers say._

L.H. plays 1°

1° only

See if the cold wind car - ries my dreams, watch you play - ing in the sun - beams.

Ah._____

Repeat ad lib. to fade

Sum - mer - time   feel - ing.)   Ah._____   Got that sum - mer - time__

feel - ing.
(Got me dream - ing,   S - Club   feel - ing.)

Verse 2:
So we're taking a drive today
Friends in the back, everything's OK.
You're my ice cream dream when we're fooling around.
Don't want this heat to ever cool down.
So ease your mind, set yourself free
Don't push what comes naturally
Making love in the afternoon
Sun's gonna shine on everything we do.

Never Had A Dream Come True

Words & Music by Cathy Dennis & Simon Ellis

use look-in' back or won-der-ing how it could be— now or might have been. All

1° only

this I know but still I can't find ways to let you— go. I nev-er had a

2° only

ways to let you— go.— I nev-er had a

dream come true 'til the day that I found—you. Ev-en though— I pre-tend— that I've moved on, you'll

Verse 2:
Somewhere in my memory
I've lost all sense of time
And tomorrow can never be
'Cause yesterday is all that fills my mind
There's no use looking back or wondering
How it should be now or might have been
All this I know but still
I can't find ways to let you go.

I never had a dream come true *etc.*

Exclusive distributors:

Music Sales Limited
8/9 Frith Street, London W1D 3JB,
England.

Music Sales Pty Limited
120 Rothschild Avenue, Rosebery, NSW 2018,
Australia.

Order No. AM973984
ISBN 0-7119-9399-8
This book © Copyright 2002 by Wise Publications.

Music arrangements by Roger Day.
Music processed by Paul Ewers Music Design.
Cover artwork courtesy of Polydor Limited (UK).

Printed in the United Kingdom by
Printwise (Haverhill) Limited, Suffolk.

Your Guarantee of Quality:
As publishers, we strive to produce every book
to the highest commercial standards.
While endeavouring to retain the original running
order of the recorded album, the book has been
carefully designed to minimise awkward page turns
and to make playing from it a real pleasure.
Particular care has been given to specifying acid-free,
neutral-sized paper made from pulps which have
not been elemental chlorine bleached.
This pulp is from farmed sustainable forests and was
produced with special regard for the environment.
Throughout, the printing and binding have been
planned to ensure a sturdy, attractive publication
which should give years of enjoyment.
If your copy fails to meet our high standards,
please inform us and we will gladly replace it.

Music Sales' complete catalogue describes thousands
of titles and is available in full colour sections by subject,
direct from Music Sales Limited.
Please state your areas of interest and send a cheque/
postal order for £1.50 for postage to: Music Sales Limited,
Newmarket Road, Bury St. Edmunds, Suffolk IP33 3YB.

www.musicsales.com